# Lincolnshire
## COUNTY COUNCIL

COMMUNITIES, CULTURAL SERVICES
and ADULT EDUCATION

**This book should be returned on or before
the last date shown below.**

KT-514-594

To renew or order library books please telephone 01522 782010
or visit www.lincolnshire.gov.uk

You will require a Personal Identification Number.
Ask any member of staff for this.

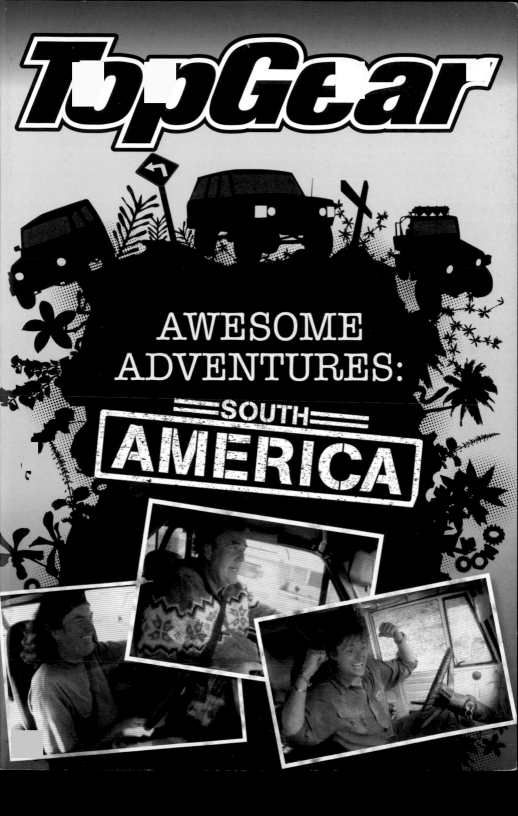

BBC Children's Books
Published by the Penguin Group
Penguin Books Ltd, 80 Strand,
London WC2R 0RL, England
Penguin Group (Australia) Ltd, 250
Camberwell Road, Camberwell, Victoria
3124, Australia (a division of Pearson
Australia Group Pty Ltd)
Canada, India, New Zealand, South
Africa

Published by BBC Children's Books, 2010
Text and design © Children's Character
Books, 2010

10 9 8 7 6 5 4 3 2 1

Adapted by Sam Philip from the BBC
*Top Gear* South America Special
television script
Internal design by Dan Newman

ISBN: 978-1-40590-700-2

Printed in Slovakia.

# CONTENTS

# INTRODUCTION

**A**s Jeremy, James and Richard skimmed up the wide, muddy Bolivian river in their narrow boat, they all had a feeling something wasn't quite right. For a start, they shouldn't even have been in a boat. They should have been transported to their destination in a fast, comfortable helicopter, but the fast, comfortable helicopter had crashed the previous day. This wasn't a good sign.

So they found themselves in a tiny, rickety canoe, chugging up a tributary of the Amazon – the most powerful river in the world – and utterly bemused by the tropical scenery and wildlife around them.

**DID YOU KNOW?**
A tributary is a stream or river that flows into a main 'parent' river. The Amazon has seven 'main' tributaries, but many thousands of smaller ones.

**Look** at that purple tree!

The **butterfly's more amazing** than your purple tree! That butterfly was the **size of a bat!**

There's a **crocodile** over there...

It's **not** a crocodile, it's a lump of wood.

Even with the breeze of the river, it was swelteringly hot.

"We're close to the Equator," realised Richard.

"We're very close to the Equator," agreed Jeremy. "Perhaps we're on it."

"No, we can't be on it," argued Richard, "or we'd see it. A big dotted line..."

Their geographical arguments were stopped short as a fat, sharp-toothed fish leapt out of the water... and straight into the boat between Richard and Jeremy, flapping furiously around on the wooden boards. As James and Richard panicked, Jeremy whipped out his bush knife.

I've **got it** with my knife! **Aha!** Is that a **piranha**?

No they're not!

That's **not** a piranha. Piranhas are long and thin.

Oh, no, that's... **sharks**.

For miles and miles the boat chugged on, ferrying them up the river and deep into the rainforest. Eventually, the boat driver veered into the river bank and dropped the three intrepid explorers on the muddy shore. He puttered off into the distance, leaving Jeremy, James and Richard alone in the middle of nowhere. Had he dropped them in the right place? There were no cars, no motorbikes, nothing but trees as far as they could see.

A few weeks earlier, they had each been given a couple of thousand pounds by the *Top Gear* producers, and told to buy any car they liked from a second-hand car website in Bolivia. The only advice was that they should make sure their purchase was four-wheel drive. Each of them had duly bought a car on the Internet, but there was no sign of any of the vehicles here. In fact, there was no sign of anything at all. They were hundreds of miles from the nearest town. Hundreds of miles from the nearest anything.

The three boys stood, silent, for a few minutes, trying to formulate a plan. And then they started to argue...

## DID YOU KNOW?

Bolivia is the fifth largest country in South America, and is entirely land-locked. Though it is four times the size of the United Kingdom, just 10,000,000 people live in Bolivia – only a sixth as many as in the UK!

**Have we just been abandoned here to die?**

**I'm sorry. On the kit front... what's that, James?**

**Are those zips? You can unzip the bottoms from your trousers?**

**That is my belt of many things.**

*TopGear*

Jeremy and Richard burst out laughing.

"What is that?" scoffed Jeremy, pointing to a small pack attached to James's belt.

"Don't touch it!" snapped James. "That's a dental healthcare kit."

"And what's this?" continued Jeremy, pointing to another pack.

"Don't touch it!" repeated James. "This... is a shoe polishing kit."

Jeremy roared with laughter. "A what?" he asked. "Well, at least if we get hungry we can eat his shoe polish."

"Basically, what you've done," said Richard slowly, "is buy a 'My First Explorer Kit' and stick it on your belt."

"Don't touch it!" repeated James, a little more annoyed this time.

Alone on the shore of the river, the three boys bickered for a while longer to pass the time. Then Richard revealed something that would prove to be a bit of an issue over the coming days.

Why? Are you **frightened** of insects?

So... all these insects. Where are they?

Yes.

Really?

You are **scared** of heights.

Yes. Don't mess about. It's a phobia. Like James and heights.

"Well what's your phobia, then?" James asked Jeremy indignantly.

"Manual labour," replied Jeremy. "You know that."

"That's not a phobia, that's... bone-idleness!" reasoned James.

"Yeah," agreed Richard. "It's not a clinical thing. It's just because you're lazy."

Bored of arguing, the three boys sat on a fallen log and waited. And waited. And waited. There was no sign of their second-hand cars, no sign of a challenge, no sign of anything. They began to wonder if the *Top Gear* producers had finally had enough of them, and had ditched them deep in the rainforest to die.

The boys argued some more, and waited some more. And some more. After several hours, James spotted something, far off down river. He stood up.

From round a bend in the river chugged a flat-topped barge, pushed by a tiny motorboat and with three battered old off-roaders perched on top. This was it: these were the cars they had ordered!

# DAY ONE

**As the barge drew closer**, it was plain that there had been a terrible mix-up. One of the off-roaders, the smallest of the bunch, was a Suzuki SJ. None of the *Top Gear* boys could have been stupid enough to choose a tiny Suzuki with which to tackle the Amazonian rainforest, could they? Could they?

## SUZUKI SJ

The Suzuki SJ is a tiny 4x4 that has been in production since 1965. Nowadays in Britain, it is known as the Suzuki Jimny. SJs have always been built around small economical engines, and aren't considered to be as good off-road as, say, a sturdy Toyota Land Cruiser. However, in 2007, a Chilean team in an SJ set a world record for the highest altitude reached by a 4x4, hitting 21,804 feet on the highest volcano in the world in South America!

James, that's the 1.3-litre special! **Famous for...**

**Yes, falling over.** I presume, then, through the **power of deduction,** that the Land Cruiser is yours, Richard?

...falling over.

The **correct** choice, as everyone will agree.

The **best** four-by-four... by far. As we know.

And **you** have bought... a Range Rover?

## LAND CRUISER

Toyota has been building Land Cruisers since 1951. It started life as a military vehicle, but was quickly adopted by civilians who wanted to go off-road. Richard's Land Cruiser is officially known as the Toyota FJ40, and was built between 1960 and 1984. Land Cruisers have always enjoyed a reputation for being indestructible... at least until the Top Gear boys got their hands on one!

"A Range Rover?" said James. "I had one of those."

"I had one as well," agreed Richard. "Did yours ever... work?

"No," said James, finally.

## RANGE ROVER

Range Rovers have been built in England since 1970. The first Range Rovers were seriously unluxurious — power steering and carpets weren't available as standard. Jeremy's car was one of the first generation of Range Rover, built between 1970 and 1996. Range Rovers have never enjoyed a reputation for being indestructible. Oh dear.

The driver of the motorboat nudged the barge alongside the riverbank, and then promptly headed off down the river, leaving the boys to figure out how to get their cars on to dry land.

"Oi!" shouted Jeremy at the boat driver, as he disappeared into the distance. "You haven't parked it!"

But it was too late. The boat driver had gone and, once again, the three boys were alone, with the barge wedged into the riverbed but with several metres of water between it and dry land. Resourcefully, the boys waded over to the barge and attempted to heave it towards shore by the ropes tied to its deck.

**Heave!**

It's no use. It's **not moving.**

The barge was wedged firm in the shallows. With its deck several feet above water, trying to get the cars off would be a very risky – and soggy – business.

Realising the barge wouldn't budge, Richard propped a gangplank up against it and hopped up on to the deck... banging his head on a thick wire as he went. Oops.

Aiming to teach Richard a lesson about coping with barges, James followed, skipping up the plank, but as he reached the top...

Eventually, even Jeremy managed to haul himself up the plank ungracefully and on to the deck. Now the boys could get their first look at the bangers they'd bought through the Bolivian classifieds. James was first to inspect his purchase: the tiny, old Suzuki SJ.

"Notoriously long-lived, sturdy, reliable, small, agile..." said James proudly, tapping the bonnet of his Suzuki.

"What did it say in the advert in the Bolivian *Auto Trader*?" asked Jeremy, refusing to believe that anyone – even James – could be daft enough to purchase a Suzuki Jimny of their own free will.

"I'll tell you what it said," admitted James. "It said the car was blue." His car was clearly red.

"Did it say in the advert that all four tyres would be pumped up?" Jeremy grinned.

"No...?" replied James, confused. He wandered round to the

other side of his car to find that its left rear tyre was flatter than, well, a very, very flat thing.

"We did buy them long distance!" Richard defended James's purchase.

But the boys soon discovered something even saggier than James's tyre, and that was the roof of Richard's Toyota. The Land Cruiser had a solid pair of front doors, but the rear of the car was covered with a ragged sheet of cloth that looked like it had been taped on by a man working in the dark. Wearing ski gloves.

"This wasn't always a convertible, was it?" James asked the obvious question.

"No," admitted Richard. "It's been... converted to a convertible. But it's a tasty car all round. I'm very pleased."

"Ooh, I like this," crowed Jeremy, tapping the passenger door of the Toyota. "The window is down here, in the door, and there's no way to wind it back up to where it should be!"

"I don't need one," replied Richard grumpily. "It's hot here."

Keen to demonstrate how foolish his friends' purchases had been, Jeremy strode confidently over to his Range Rover.

"Behold, gentlemen, the 3.9-litre V8 engine," said Jeremy smugly, lifting the bonnet of the Range Rover to reveal an oily, dirty engine bay.

"Ahem," coughed James gently, "the 3.9-litre, eh? They had injection, didn't they Hammond?"

"Yep," agreed Richard.

"Yes, all of them were fuel-injected," agreed Jeremy proudly.

"Then what are those on top?" asked James, pointing to the engine.

"I believe they're... carburettors, aren't they?" answered Richard.

"They look like carburettors," smiled James.

## DID YOU KNOW?

The carburettor is the device that blends fuel and air in an engine. Carburettors were found on almost every car from the late 1800s until the 1980s, when they were replaced by fuel injection.

"They are carburettors!" said Jeremy in disbelief. He'd been delivered a cheaper, worse Range Rover.

"That can't be a 3.9-litre engine," crowed Richard, laughing at Jeremy's misfortune. Or stupidity, maybe. "That's a 3.5!"

"It said in the advert that it was a 3.9!" complained Jeremy.

"Well, it said mine was blue!" countered James.

"Well, you'll be opening the bonnet a lot on this," Richard said to Jeremy. "That's what killed these cars off. Why, whenever you go anywhere inhospitable in the world, does everyone use a Toyota Land Cruiser?"

Still arguing about who had made the worst purchase, the three boys scrambled awkwardly back down the ramp and on to the shore. From the depths of the jungle, a mysterious man in a white coat emerged, carrying an envelope. This, finally, was the boys' challenge.

Jeremy took the envelope, and the mysterious man disappeared off into the undergrowth. "OK," he said, clearing his throat. "It says...

That was it. Short, simple, but very scary. James and Richard looked bemused.

"So we have to go a thousand miles..." Jeremy tailed off as he pointed his arm west, in the direction of the Pacific. All they could see, right the way to the horizon, was dense greenery. No road, no track, no path.

## THE CHALLENGE:

You are in Bolivia, and you will drive to the Pacific Ocean, which is one thousand miles away.

"There's a jungle in the way," realised Richard, grimly. But there was more than jungle. There were active volcanoes, lifeless deserts and perilous mountain passes to conquer before they reached the Pacific Ocean.

But first, they had to get their cars off the barge. The three boys jumped into the thigh-deep water and tried to haul the barge closer to shore, but Jeremy swiftly ran into trouble...

**I'm sinking!** I can't pull myself out!

Every time the bubbles come out, you go in **deeper.**

I know! **Help!**

As Jeremy sank deeper into the river, the water rising past his waist, Richard and James became so concerned that they collapsed with laughter.

"Go and get a rope!" panicked Jeremy, clinging desperately on to the barge. "Something to tie around my waist!"

"All right, we'll get something," said Richard grudgingly. And then he came up with a brilliant idea: how about pulling Jeremy out of the water... using his own Range Rover?

You want a **proper** knot, don't you?

**Hammond!** What are you doing?

Do you think it'll start?

**No!** Just any old knot!

The Range Rover didn't start. As Richard worked the key in the ignition, it coughed and spluttered and, eventually, fell dead again. Jeremy sank deeper into the mud. The water was now up around his stomach, and rising fast.

"You bought the wrong car," called James unhelpfully from the deck of the barge, as Richard again fired the ignition. This time, the Range Rover growled into life, and Richard slid it into reverse.

**Backwards! Ow! My arms! Stop! Stop!** My jeans are ruined.

Jeremy's jeans might have been ruined, but at least he was safely out of the mud. The cars, though, were still sitting uselessly on the raft. So, with half the day already gone, the boys needed a new plan for getting their 4x4s onto shore.

"You know, in the Second World War, when a submarine was grounded," started Jeremy, "they used to get the crew to run backwards and forwards, and it would sort of shuffle it along."

"You're suggesting we run backwards and forwards on the barge?" asked Richard, unimpressed.

"No," said Jeremy. "We use the cars. If we go to the back of the barge, that weighs it down and lifts the front up. We then charge forwards, which shuffles the barge nearer to the bank in front."

"That's a good idea!" replied Richard, astonished.

The three boys jumped in their cars, turned the keys in the ignitions and...

**Oh no.** Has anybody got any jump leads? **It won't start.**

"I just want to get this completely clear," huffed Jeremy. "My Range Rover is working well – it's already saved a man's life. Richard's Land Cruiser? Broken down. Oh no! Smoke! Quite a lot of smoke!"

Richard had finally coaxed some signs of life from his Land Cruiser, but they weren't good signs. Smoke was billowing out from the bonnet.

"The starter motor's burnt out," announced Richard, gloomily. His car wouldn't be starting for a while.

As the sun sank low in the sky, Jeremy came up with a solution. "Why don't we tie your Land Cruiser to the back of my Range Rover?" he asked.

"I'd rather drown myself," growled Richard. This, he realised, would be admitting that Jeremy had bought the better car. "Oh, all right, let's do it."

It was nearly dark by the time Jeremy had inched his Range Rover into position and tied the rope to the Land Cruiser for the most ambitious jump-start in history. "Three, two, one... go!" he shouted, revving his Range Rover and hauling the Toyota along the deck.

As the jungle faded to pitch black, Jeremy tried over and over to budge the raft towards the shore by revving his Range Rover from one end of the boat to the other with the Land Cruiser dragged helplessly behind. Again and again, the Toyota thumped into the back of Jeremy's Range Rover, but were they making any progress?

# DAY TWO

No. Despite all of Jeremy's efforts, the morning sun revealed the results: absolutely nothing. The barge was still exactly where it had been the night before.

But, on the plus side, Jeremy and Richard had found a peanut plant, and were greedily scoffing from it. As they ate, James made a discovery.

"These planks," he started, pointing at pieces of wood on-board the barge, "are longer than this one we've been falling off. If we put two together, they'll be long enough to reach the shore."

Soon enough, the boys had constructed a pair of wobbly, rudimentary ramps from the side of the barge to the shore, a pair of planks spaced the width of a set of tyres apart. Could they support the weight of a car? Or would they snap, plunging the boys' 4x4s into the river? As chief engineer, James was the first to find out.

He inched the front wheels of his Suzuki on to the ramp, hanging his head out the window in a desperate attempt to see where he was driving.

Jeremy and Richard watched anxiously as James edged onto the ramps, checking his wheels were aligned with the planks of wood. "You're all right!" shouted Richard from the shore, and James floored the accelerator. With a wobbly lunge, the Suzuki slid down the ramps and onto dry land.

"Yes!" cheered Richard. He'd made it!

Well, nearly. As the Suzuki's back wheels reached the shore and James accelerated to make his way up the bank, the Suzuki's wheels spun helplessly and it wedged itself down into the boggy sand. It was firmly stuck.

"Four-wheel drive!" shouted Jeremy

"It is four-wheel drive, you half-wit!" shouted James back at him.

"Then why aren't the front wheels turning?" asked Jeremy.

"Oh, don't tell me it doesn't work..." said James, resignedly.

His four-wheel drive didn't work. James was stuck. And, worse still, he was blocking the ramp, meaning Richard and Jeremy couldn't get their cars off by the same route. Grumpily, they grabbed more planks to build another pair of ramps beside the originals. When the second set of ramps was ready, Jeremy was next to go.

Tiny tickle to the left...

British engineering, **don't** let me down.

**Here we go!**

"Now that's what I call four-wheel drive!" yelled Jeremy triumphantly as the Range Rover scrambled up the bank and into the fringes of the jungle. Finally, one of their cars was off the boat and ready to roll. And, even better, he could now tow James's stranded Suzuki out of trouble.

"Please be gentle with this, Jeremy, and not a yob," pleaded James, as Jeremy attached the tow rope to the front of the Suzuki. "POWER!" bellowed Jeremy as he flattened the throttle and yanked James and his Suzuki free of the mud. The heroic Range Rover had done it again! But...

**Stop! Stop!**

**Clarkson, you pillock...**

Jeremy had towed James straight into a log, but that was nothing compared to what Richard was about to endure. With no power and no brakes, Richard and his Toyota would have to rely on Jeremy and his Range Rover to pull them off the boat. This would be a delicate operation, and Jeremy wasn't very good at delicate.

**Oh, dear God.**

**No!**

**Are you ready?**

**Right, he's ready.**

As carefully as he could, Jeremy slid forward. The rope between the Range Rover and the Toyota tightened, and the Land Cruiser creaked to the top of the ramp. As Richard winced in terror, Jeremy accelerated, dragging Richard and his Toyota over the edge...

Yeahhhh!!!

Finally, all three cars were on the shore. To celebrate, the boys cracked open the big metal box that had been sitting on the deck of the boat.

"Chainsaw... winch... rubber tubing," said Jeremy as he hauled each of the items from the crate. "What kind of party are they planning?"

They loaded the box into the back of Jeremy's Range Rover, which then jump-started Richard's Toyota. With a splutter, the Land Cruiser cranked into life. It was alive! After a day of frustration, it was time to hit the road. Or, rather, the undergrowth.

"Jungle!" yelled Jeremy, pointing to the thick canopy behind them. In convoy, the three 4x4s ploughed into the dense rainforest. Finally, they were underway, on the way to the Pacific Ocean.

Slowly. Without even a hint of road or track, progress was slow. Every few metres, one of the boys had to jump out of their car and hack a thick branch or vine out the way so the convoy could proceed. It was tough, sweaty work, but after a day of sitting on the bank of the Amazon, they didn't care. Hour after hour, they chopped and slashed their way through the thicket, gulping water and mopping their brows every few seconds. They were on their way. They were jungle heroes!

"Guys," said Jeremy, after a tough afternoon of toil through the undergrowth. "I left my mobile phone down by the river."

"You dipstick!" replied James.

"I'm going to have to go back and get it," said Jeremy. "Just wait here. I'll go get it..."

He wandered off, back down the track. Fifteen seconds later, Jeremy appeared beside Richard and James. "Got it!" he said, happily. It was exactly where he'd left it: on the tree stump next to the barge.

At that moment, the boys realised how slow their progress was. In three hours of slashing and cutting, they'd managed to cover about twenty metres. This wasn't fast enough: they had to cover at least one hundred miles every day, and in nearly two days, they'd managed less than the length of a swimming pool. At this rate, it'd take them centuries to reach the Pacific!

But luckily, after another twenty minutes of slashing and hacking, the boys found a logging track, a rough road running through the jungle that allowed them to pick up the speed. Not very much, but a bit. Now they had a chance to get to know their cars.

> **DID YOU KNOW?**
> The Amazon rainforest creates around 15 per cent of the world's new oxygen. That's why scientists call it 'the lungs of the planet'!

Time to find out **what's working.** All these dials in the middle... **no.** Speedo... **no.** That said, I seem to have bought the **only** 1980s Range Rover in the world that **works!**

You're probably looking at this Suzuki and thinking **'It's a toy off-roader'.** But I'll tell you what it is. It's plucky. **Look** at Jeremy's Range Rover, lumbering along. This is like a **little mountain goat.** It just... skips along.

Land Cruisers are **legendarily** reliable and bullet proof. **This one... isn't.** Temperature gauge? **Not working.** Fuel gauge? Don't know. Brakes? **Not working.** That makes this one **more special.** I have bought the **only** malfunctioning Land Cruiser in the **world.**

As afternoon turned to evening, the boys ploughed on along the narrow path, enjoying driving at last after nearly two days of frustrating waiting. For mile after mile they bumped on through the dense greenery, their headlights picking a path through the jungle as night crept around them.

But, even in the pitch dark, it was still seriously hot. Sticky, damp, sweaty heat that made the boys' cars near unbearable: with no air conditioning in any of the vehicles, the best they could do was wind down the windows and hope for a bit of a breeze. There wasn't one.

"How can it be this hot at midnight?" shouted Jeremy from the lead car. There wasn't anyone to hear. "How is that possible?"

But in the car behind, Richard had more to worry about than the heat.

Plagued by huge buzzing insects, Richard insisted they made camp for the night. They parked up, pitched their tents... and Jeremy began to read a bedtime story to cheer Richard up.

**What is that?** There's something in here SQUEAKING at me! **I can't stand that! I've got to get out!**

This is a book about all the **creatures** that live in the rainforest. Would you like to hear about... the **Brazilian wandering spider?**

Not really, **no.**

"It causes around five human fatalities a year," continued Jeremy, ignoring Richard. "It lives on the forest floor... ooh, how about the botfly?" he said cheerily, turning to a page picturing a giant-eyed insect. "A marvellous thing. The botfly cannot sting a human directly, but captures smaller insects, lays its larvae upon them and then releases them. If the smaller host insect then bites the human, the botfly larvae are impregnated into the skin. The larvae then grow inside the skin and then EAT their way out. The BBC *Natural History Unit* reports the case of a man who was bitten behind the ear and then kept awake at night by the sound of the botfly larvae eating the flesh inside his head..."

Richard gulped. He shone his torch around their camp. Everything – their tents, their cars, their clothes – was crawling in huge insects. He shivered. This wasn't going to be a good night's sleep. Several hours later...

What's that? **Arrgh! Stick insect!** Something just flew in my hair. **It's big!**

# DAY THREE

**T**hings didn't get much **better** for Richard the next day. In the bright light of an early morning, he stepped blearily from his tent, brushing his teeth and wearing trousers that looked different to the night before...

**Who** has done this?

Ooh, there's a **snake** in your car. It's known locally as the **Big Vicious Killer Snake.**

And things went from bad to worse. As Richard opened the door to climb into his car, he noticed something slithering around the gear lever.

"Er... guys?" he called, nervously. Jeremy and James wandered over.

The boys waited for the snake to slither out of Richard's car and off into the undergrowth. After checking their cars for any other poisonous animals, they hit the road again. Not that it was really a road at all. It wasn't even a track.

Bumpily, slowly, they edged on through the thick rainforest. Strangely, Richard's missing trouser leg hadn't reappeared. He radioed Jeremy in the car ahead.

Richard's missing trouser leg

**Seriously,** who's got my trouser leg?

Your trouser leg is **missing?**

For a few hours, Jeremy led the way, his heavy Range Rover clearing a path for James and Richard. But the strain of being out in front started to take its toll on the Range Rover.

"This is now smelling hot, this car," realised Jeremy, the stench of an overheating engine wafting in through the open windows.

"I can smell Jeremy's Range Rover from back here!" coughed James from the car behind. "It smells of... imminent failure."

And James was right. A couple of minutes later, the Range Rover's engine died and Jeremy coasted to a halt. James eased to a stop behind him and  – THWACK! – was bumped from behind by Richard.

"That wasn't very funny three series ago!" James shouted at Richard. "It really isn't funny now."

"I'm not doing it on purpose!" protested Richard. "I haven't got any brakes. That's how I stop!"

Jeremy lifted the bonnet of the Range Rover. Things didn't look good.

Oh no, it's **broken!**

What a **rotten** bit of luck.

**It's your fault.** I've been forging a path through this stuff, bamboo has got in, **broken** my fan and now **my engine's overheated.**

"The plucky Brit has wounded itself helping you out!" continued Jeremy.

"Your plucky British car has been defeated by a piece of – what was it? – bamboo," argued James. "What sort of a design is that if a piece of bamboo can get up there and break the fan? Bamboo!"

"Without this," said Jeremy, tapping the Range Rover and pointing at Richard, "would you still be on the boat?"

Richard nodded guiltily.

"And would you," continued Jeremy, turning his attention to James, "still be stuck on the river bank?"

James nodded too.

"This car," concluded Jeremy triumphantly, "is the hero of the day."

By the time they'd finished bickering, the Range Rover had cooled down and they could carry on with their battle through the undergrowth. It was tough going: every few hundred yards, the mini-convoy would stop for one of the boys to leap from the car and hack back the undergrowth with a machete. After a few hours of tiring, tough progress, they encountered a hazard that would require a lot more than a machete.

**DID YOU KNOW?**
The Amazon basin – the area drained by the Amazon river and its tributaries – is over a billion acres in size. If it was a country, it'd be the ninth largest in the world!

It was a gully, a deep ravine that ran directly across their path, each side a sheer drop of some twenty feet into a flat, dried-out riverbed. Heading off the edge in any of their cars would be idiotic: they would simply get jammed at the bottom. But that wasn't stopping Jeremy.

"I'm going to drive down it and up the other side," he announced decisively, having inspected the gully for a good five or six seconds.

"No," sighed Richard. "You can't!"

"The biggest strength with the Range Rover," said Jeremy

confidently, "is that the wheel hits the bottom before the front of the car does. If you look at a Porsche Cayenne or... your car, Richard, there's about eighteen feet of bonnet in front of the wheels."

"This car," Richard decided to put it simply, "cannot do that. You won't make it."

Jeremy wasn't to be swayed. "You two," he said, finally, "stand back. Watch and learn."

He jumped into his Range Rover and strapped in. "If you believe something will happen," he told himself, "it will happen."

And with that, he released the handbrake and set off into the gully.

"Brilliant!" mocked Richard from the top of the gully. "Now you're stuck in a hole."

And Jeremy was. Firmly stuck, with the nose of his Range Rover jammed in the bottom of the gully and his rear wheels on the bank.

**CRASH!**

**Oh dear.**

**I knew that a while back.**

**You dozy, woolly-haired pillock!** He's going to need winching out, you know that?

James fired up the winch on his Suzuki, which was still sat safely at the top of the gully, and threw the end of the cable down to Jeremy, who attached it firmly to the back bumper of the Range Rover. James flicked the winch's switch and stood back to watch his Suzuki's moment of heroism.

The cable started to coil back round the winch, hauling the two cars closer together... but the Range Rover wasn't budging an inch. What was going on?

The lighter Suzuki had winched itself into the ditch, falling on top of the heavier Range Rover. Both the cars were now stuck: no matter how many times James tried to reverse his Suzuki up the steep bank, it kept crashing back down into the Range Rover.

**James! Stop it!**

You'll have to drive it out.

It **won't** stop.

It **won't** drive out.

It was down to Hammond and his Toyota, the only car left at the top of the gully. He attached his winch to the back of James's car, and easily hauled the Suzuki out backwards to the top of the ditch. Next, with a little more difficulty, came the Range Rover.

**Look** at my little donkey, pulling the **Range Rover** out! **Aha!**

**Oh, yes!**

So, despite all the winching and crashing, the boys and their cars were still on the wrong side of the impassable gully. They realised they would have to build a bridge... which made one of them very happy.

After Jeremy had felled four tall trees, the three boys set about constructing their bridge. All afternoon they toiled, chopping the trees to the right size and lashing them together. After that came the all-important safety testing procedure.

Because James had the lightest car, he was nominated to make the first crossing. By the time he had lined up his Suzuki's front wheels at the edge of the makeshift bridge,

**I declare this... strong.** Get in your car and drive over, James.

the rainforest was getting dark. James inched onto the bridge, listening out for instructions from Jeremy and Richard. Their instructions weren't very helpful, and it was a long way down into the ravine below.

So that's exactly what James did. As the Suzuki hung

On this side I would say... **not left.**

A little bit left, James.

At this point, I'd engage MAXIMUM POWER!

Left or not left?

unsteadily over the deep gully, he mashed the accelerator. The Suzuki wobbled and slipped... and then, nervously, skittered along the bridge and up the other side of the gully. He'd made it!

But their happiness was short-lived. It was nearly dark, and Jeremy was next to go, in his much heavier – and much wider – Range Rover. He switched on his headlights and edged the big car nervously onto the ramp. In the inky twilight, the instructions from the far bank were getting worse...

**Left hand down!**

**I can't see the back wheel.**

**It's not looking good from where I am!**

Slowly, inch by inch, Jeremy was making progress across the bridge. It was scary stuff: one wrong move and the Range Rover would plunge off the bridge and down into the gully far below. That would hurt. As he neared the bank on the other side, Jeremy, like James, floored the throttle and scrambled back on to firm land. They were two-thirds there!

**That was scary.**

But surely it would be even worse for Richard? At least Jeremy had the benefit of a tiny bit of sunlight. As Richard lined up his Toyota on to the bridge, it was properly, completely dark.

"Hammond, I'm afraid we simply can't see anything," shouted Jeremy from the far bank. "We don't know where you are!"

But Richard had to go. He teetered onto the bridge, every muscle clenched with fear.

**Stop!**

**This is quite frightening.**

**I've got no brakes!**

**ARRRRGGH!**

Out of control, the Toyota careered along the ramp with Richard trying desperately to keep it in line. With a fearful creak, the left side of the bridge slipped in the mud. Would it tip Richard and his car into the gully? No! With a welcome squelch, the Toyota's front tyres grabbed the bank of the gully and Richard powered up to freedom. They'd done it!

But the boys couldn't stop and make camp. With so much time lost crossing the gully, they had to push on through the night if they were to make it to the Pacific before the end of the century.

Deep in darkness, the three cars rolled on through the jungle, flicking branches and bumping over thick roots as they went. Jeremy decided he was fed up with the jungle.

## DID YOU KNOW?

More than half of the world's ten million species of plants, animals and insects live in the Amazon rainforest.

**GRRRRRR!**

Several hours later, the boys made camp for the night. Before he crawled into his tent for a few hours of fitful, sweaty sleep, Jeremy decided to solve his Range Rover's overheating problem... by cutting a couple of huge holes in the bonnet using the angle grinder they had been provided with. But as the sparks flew from the metal, something very, very bad happened...

**FZZZZHH!!**

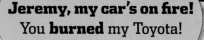

**Jeremy, my car's on fire!** You **burned** my Toyota!

After failing to douse the flames with a can of drink, Jeremy remembered there was a fire extinguisher in the boot of his car. But, as he sprayed the canvas cover of the Toyota with foam, the damage was already done. Richard's convertible wouldn't be providing any cover from now on.

# DAY FOUR

Jeremy and Richard were woken early by the sounds of the jungle: the tweeting of birds, the chirruping of insects... and the thrum of motorbikes. Strange. Blearily, they dressed in their filthy, sticky clothes and unzipped James's tent. James blinked sleepily and emerged, still holding his machete.

"Er, James," said Jeremy, sheepishly. "What we've done is... accidentally camped on a road."

As he spoke, a local man on an ancient motorcycle zipped through the middle of their camp.

"Morning!" Hammond greeted him cheerily, but the local man didn't look very impressed. They had to move... and quickly.

Ten minutes later, they were off, clanking through the jungle in their ancient, battered 4x4s. The atmosphere was, well, smelly: the boys' clothes were caked in dirt and jungle-stuff, and none of them had showered in four days.

**DID YOU KNOW?**
The Amazon river is just over 4,000 miles long. This makes it the second-longest river in the world: only the Nile is longer.

Their shower arrived unannounced. In seconds, the sky turned from blue to black, and the rain began: not a few gentle droplets, but a mighty thunderstorm that immediately turned their dirt track to mud. In his Toyota, under a badly burned canopy, Richard wasn't enjoying the downpour.

And things were about to get a whole lot wetter. A mile on, the three cars drew to a halt as the road ran out. In front of them lay a river, several hundred metres across and swelled by the biblical

Hammond, how **wet** are you getting in this rain?

Very wet

It's **not bad** actually...

rain. It wasn't the Amazon itself, but it was big. There was no bridge, and no way around it. They would have to drive across... but they had no idea how deep it was.

Richard went first. The first hundred metres or so were easy, the water lapping barely halfway up the Toyota's wheels. But then the river started to get deeper.

**Now, do I follow** in Hammond's wheel-marks on the basis we know how deep it is, or do I think **'he's an incompetent fool'** and go somewhere else?

*TopGear*

Jeremy, certain that Hammond was indeed an incompetent fool, decided to chart his own course across the river, and immediately ran into trouble. Trouble in the shape of some very deep water. Who was the incompetent fool now?

**That's looking DEEP!**

**Please keep going,** little donkey. **Swim, swim!**

Richard's route was looking better, but not much...

As Jeremy's Range Rover spluttered in the depths of the river, the Toyota soldiered on.

"This is when the Land Cruiser suddenly comes into its own," said Richard smugly, as he reached the safety of shallower waters. "Yes, there may be more comfortable things that'll get you there, but the Land Cruiser will always get you home..."

Back in the middle of the river, Jeremy was looking in very real danger of never getting home at all.

ARRRGGH!

Foolishly, James had followed Jeremy's route, and was now trapped behind the lifeless Range Rover. The only way he could get past and to the other side was to steer into even deeper water,

**It's stopped! Aargh!** Water's coming **in** to my car!

a tactic that surely couldn't end well in the smallest car.

"You're going to have to go round the outside!" shouted Jeremy as he hung out the window of his Range Rover, trying to stay dry. "I'll tell you when to turn. Go on, good... there!"

But James wasn't there. In fact, he was stuck too, in a yet deeper section of the river. Richard, having parked his Toyota up on the far bank, had waded back across on foot to watch his two friends making a giant mess of their crossing.

**Jeremy, why did I listen to you? You imbecile!**

**Good...** that's two cars stuck.

Too proud to accept the offer of a winch from Richard's Toyota, Jeremy tried over and over to restart his Range Rover. Finally, improbably, it fired into life, spraying water from the engine as it did.

Slowly, Jeremy glugged towards shallower water, leaving a clear path for James's Suzuki to reach the far bank. Somehow the Suzuki began to float and, damply, James made his way across the river to rejoin Jeremy and Richard. James wasn't very happy with Jeremy.

If you hadn't tried to be so **clever,** and your car hadn't been so **unreliable**, I wouldn't have had to go round the outside in my small off-roader, **and I wouldn't have sunk!**

The **rainforest** is **just getting worse...**

## DID YOU KNOW?

An area of rainforest the size of a football pitch is cut down every second by loggers. This forest will never regrow. Scientists believe that around 140 species of plant, animal and insect are driven to extinction every day by deforestation. That's 50,000 species a year!

"But I'll tell you something. If you look over there," continued Jeremy, pointing west and cheerily ignoring James's rant, "wouldn't you say it was getting thinner?"

He was right. As the cars dripped their way along the dirt track, the undergrowth became less thick and the trees less frequent. They had reached the edge of the rainforest! Better still, as the woods turned to scrubland, they found a gravel track heading in the right direction. It was almost a real road! For a few minutes, everything seemed perfect: they were out of the spider-infested sweatbox that was the rainforest, and onto a proper track where they could pick up some proper speed and cover some proper miles.

And then James and Richard discovered a problem. Dust.

Oh, God!

The dust kicked up from the road was filling their cars and eyes and throats, blinding and choking them as they drove. To make matters worse, the road surface was terrible, bouncing them about like pebbles in a washing machine. But Jeremy, in the only car with a proper roof and working windows, couldn't see what the problem was.

"Answer me this simple question," he buzzed over the walkie-talkies. "How comfortable are you two... right now?"

It's like a **big feather mattress. I** really am **relaxing.**

But Richard wasn't relaxing. His car was full of dust, jiggling around like a power drill and, to make matters worse, constantly rattling.

"I'm so sick of that noise!" he screamed to himself through the dust. "Stop rattling at me!"

Behind, in his smooth, dust-free Range Rover, Jeremy turned up his iPod and breathed a deep, relaxed sigh. At last, they were really on the move, making progress to the Pacific. And, best of all, in just a couple of hours they would soon reach a town where they could get a proper night's sleep and – most importantly – a shower...

# DAY FIVE

The next morning, things were looking good. The three boys had, for the first time in nearly a week, enjoyed a good sleep and a shower, and they were off to rack up some good miles on a road hopefully free of rivers, ravines or poisonous snakes. Over the dusty scrubland, their cars were running sweetly – or, at least, as sweetly as a trio of battered old 4x4s could be expected to run. At long last, they were having fun.

Until the road began to climb. As the gradient got steeper and steeper, Jeremy's Range Rover started to sounded very unwell.

"Every time we go up any form of gradient for any period of time," he explained, "the engine gets very, very warm."

A warm engine was bad. The higher the road climbed, the more Jeremy began to lose power, and the more the Range Rover smelled of burning. With no time to stop and mend the engine properly, Jeremy decided on a radical solution.

> The scope of my engineering **genius** knows no bounds. **The vents I cut in the bonnet are now windows!** I can see where I'm going, the engine is cool and all is well.

Behind in his Suzuki, James wasn't so convinced.

"Sooner or later," he announced, "Jeremy will have to admit that his Range Rover isn't actually working properly."

Jeremy, of course, was going to do no such thing. They were now only a hundred miles from La Paz, the Bolivian capital, the highest city in the world. Unfortunately, those hundred miles were up what the locals called the Camino de la Muerta – 'The Death Road'. This was the most dangerous road in the world, a wonky track cut into a sheer cliff face that tumbled thousands of feet to the valley floor below. The terrifying drops, the boys knew, had claimed hundreds of lives over the years... and they had to tackle it in their rickety 4x4s.

**DID YOU KNOW?**
The Death Road is officially known as the North Yungas Road. It stretches about forty miles from Corioco to the Bolivian capital La Paz, and rises over two miles. Some of the sheer drops measure over 200 metres from top to bottom! Experts estimate that between 200-300 people die every year on the road.

James, especially, was nervous. Not only because he was scared of heights, but because, as the boys pulled to a halt at the bottom of the Death Road, his car wasn't looking in good shape.

**James, I don't know much about the rear suspension design on Suzukis...**

**...but the shock absorbers are traditionally attached at BOTH ends. Yours is bouncing around on the spring.**

Rirhard was right. A big, vital-looking piece of metal, one of the most important elements of the Suzuki's rear suspension, was dangling from the bottom of James's car. This, Richard knew, would make the Suzuki almost impossible to drive.

"I'm glad you said that up here, on my favourite road," said James sarcastically, knowing there was nothing he could do about his suspension now. He'd have to tackle the Death Road with a broken car and hope for the best.

"Before you go," continued James, more seriously now, "I genuinely don't like heights. You know that you drive into the back of my car and it's a very funny joke..."

Richard nodded sheepishly.

"You want ME to drive into the back of it?" asked Jeremy.

"No," snapped James. He wasn't finding this amusing. "Don't do it or I will cut your head off."

"I can understand that," said Richard, jumping into his Toyota. It was time to tackle the Death Road.

Well, not quite. Jeremy's voice came over Richard's walkie-talkie.

**OK,** here I come. Careful, careful, careful...

"My car," he said, "is perfect in every way apart from it not starting. So could you... er, push me a little bit?"

Hammond smiled. "So you want me... to push you... with my car... on this road here?"

"Yes," replied Jeremy nervously. "There's no alternative..."

**Oh,** I wasn't as careful as I could have been. Sorry!

But the bump did the trick, and the three cars were on their way up the Death Road. Very soon, they learned why the road had earned its name and its reputation. Wooden crosses stood at the side of the road, marking where people had gone over the edge. The drops were gigantic, dizzying, and there was no rail or barrier to stop a rusty old SUV from plummeting over them.

They were scared, all three of them. But, the boys realised, so long as they stayed on the inside of the road and took things slowly, they would be OK. Scared, yes, but OK.

And then the trucks came, charging down the hill, kicking up dust and pushing the three boys and their unreliable

That is HIGH! That is a **massive, massive drop.**

Oh, that's **narrow!** I don't know what I'm doing!

I **don't know** the rules! It's completely **baffling...**

*TopGear*

4x4s towards the cliff edge.

But still they progressed, nervously, up the Death Road. High above the valley floor, James found himself behind a wide truck, crawling up the inside of the road.

"I've got to go past him," he muttered nervously. He swung out on to the scary side of the road and accelerated past the truck. The right-hand side of his car was inches from the edge of the cliff. There was no margin for error. Gradually, sweatily, he eased past the truck and back onto the safe side of the road.

James realised he'd been holding his breath for the entire overtaking manoeuvre. "Breathe!" he muttered to himself. The higher they climbed, the more broken Richard's Toyota became.

James's Suzuki was faring even worse. After a couple of hours of climbing, it shuddered to a halt at the side of the road.

I'm **inches from death** and the steering wheel doesn't **do** anything!

"What's the matter?" asked Jeremy, parking up and wandering over.

"It's got dirt in the fuel system from the river," explained James, opening the bonnet.

My brakes don't **stop** me and I can't **breathe** because of the dust. That's **real fear** now...

"So it's broken?" asked Jeremy, mockingly.

"No, it's not broken!" argued James.

"Your simple cheap car is broken," said Jeremy finally, and

jumped back in his Range Rover. He sped off up the mountain, leaving James and Richard to fix the broken Suzuki.

Once they had restarted the Suzuki, James and Richard decided to stick together. As buses and trucks barrelled down the road towards them, they clung to the inside of the road, as tight as they could to the cliff wall. But suddenly...

**KKRNTCH**

No problem, thought Richard, because James – who had just parked up behind him – would winch him free in a jiffy. Wouldn't he?

"Er, hold on," said James apologetically, holding a big, broken

Right. **I'm in a ditch.** OK. Didn't see that **one** coming.

switch. "My winch isn't working..."

Far ahead, Jeremy was stretching out a lead over the other two.

"I'm all on my own on Death Road," he realised, as he climbed higher and higher. "I have no idea where the other two are. They have no phones, they're not on the radio. They could be dead..."

**DID YOU KNOW?**
The Death Road is now a popular tourist attraction for cyclists. If you start at the top, you can cover almost forty miles before you need to pedal. However, it's very dangerous – over a dozen cyclists have died on the road in the last decade.

Further down the valley, death was looking like a very serious possibility for James and Richard. As they waited for a truck driver to drag the Toyota free, the hundreds of locals caught in the traffic jam – the traffic jam caused by Richard – were getting angry. As the Toyota was hauled free of the ditch, Richard and James set off up the road as quickly as possible, avoiding eye contact with anyone.

But pretty soon, Richard wished he was still stuck in the ditch.

A long way ahead, Jeremy had reached 5500 feet above sea level – over a mile straight up – and was about to discover first-hand just how dicey the Death Road could be. Under a waterfall, on an especially narrow section, he met another car...

But the other car didn't stop. It inched forwards, pushing Jeremy closer and closer to the edge.

**God, no! Stop there!**

That is **slipping.** That is **going...**

**Phew!**

The rocks under Jeremy's wheels – the very edge of the cliff – broke loose and tumbled off into the valley, crashing to the valley floor thousands of feet below. But still the other car kept on inching into him. Jeremy had no choice but to push on... and hope the road held. Millimetre by millimetre he edged forwards, stones crumbling beneath his tyres, the Range Rover tipping towards the abyss below. But eventually...

Far behind, James and Richard crept on, expecting to catch up with Jeremy eventually. But they didn't. Day became night, and they found themselves scuttling up the world's most dangerous road in sheer darkness. This clearly wasn't a good idea, and to make matters worse, the Suzuki's battery was failing, leaving James's headlights getting dimmer and dimmer...

**This is murder!**

Soon, the inevitable happened. James's battery fizzled out, leaving his car dead. Knowing they needed to press on, and that his Toyota's alternator could recharge James's battery, Richard switched around the batteries on the two cars.

**I think** it was pretty good of me to **donate** my battery.

This time, we're **not** going to run with your headlights on.

Yes it was.

**OK.** We'll use the torches.

*TopGear*

> I've **waited** until nightfall at the summit of **Death Road,** and my colleagues aren't here. **Which means they must be dead.** Therefore, I've made them these **touching memorials.**

Unaware of James and Richard's mechanical troubles, Jeremy had reached the summit of Death Road, and had made camp for the night. But James and Richard weren't dead. Not yet. But as he followed Richard's Toyota up the Death Road with only a pair of tiny torches to light his way, James thought the end might be near. He buzzed Richard on the walkie-talkie:

> Hammond, I want to **say something** to you that I wouldn't say at **any** other time.

> What?

> **Please don't leave me.**

# DAY SIX

**R**ichard didn't leave James. They survived the Death Road – just – and, the next morning, were reunited with Jeremy in La Paz, Bolivia's capital and the world's highest city.

## LA PAZ

La Paz is the biggest city in Bolivia, and is home to almost a million people – nearly a tenth of the country's population. It stands at a height of 12,000 feet above sea level – that's over two miles high!

As they sat in a café, waiting for their next set of instructions from one of the mysterious men in white jackets, Jeremy couldn't help noticing that the atmosphere was slightly... frosty. The mysterious man in the white jacket duly appeared, handed over an envelope, and scuttled off out of sight.

Jeremy opened it and cleared his throat.

Are you ready?

No.

I couldn't go back to a hotel, eat a steak and go to bed **feeling good about myself** if I'd just left my mates to **die.**

**I still haven't forgiven you.** We're not going to be all matey and **forget** that you **abandoned us to die.** Just so you know.

And tell your mates the next morning that the pepper steak **wasn't** very good.

"I had to go to bed!" protested Jeremy. "I thought you were dead. I had a simple ceremony for you. I said kind words about you."

Richard and James looked unimpressed.

"What are we doing?" snapped Richard, gesturing at the envelope. "Go on."

Jeremy read from the envelope.

Between La Paz and the Pacific Ocean, there is the Altiplano, where the altitude will cause you to have a pulmonary oedema. Then there's the Andes where you will have a cerebral oedema, and then the Atacama, which is fifty times drier than Death Valley. It has never rained. It is the driest place on Earth, and there is no life. Not even bacteria.

The boys were very quiet for a while. Pulmonary oedemas and cerebral oedemas and lifeless deserts didn't sound very good. They sat for a while, thinking about the dangers that lay ahead... and then decided they'd better get on with modifying their cars. They set off in search of a workshop, and worked through the day and into the night to prepare their cars for altitude, mountains and desert.

## DID YOU KNOW?

A pulmonary oedema is the medical term for 'fluid in the lungs'. It makes breathing very difficult, and if untreated can lead to a coma or even death. A cerebral oedema is the medical term for 'water in the brain'. It can be caused by high altitude, and results in sickness, headaches and unconsciousness. No wonder the boys were looking nervous!

I've **lifted** the Land Cruiser. It gives me room for the **bigger, wider tyres** I need for the desert sand. Roll cage for safety, **obviously,** and then to get rid of the weight, **I've lost the doors.** They were steel and very heavy. And the roof, **and anything else I didn't need.**

# DAY SEVEN

**E**arly the next morning, they set out in convoy in their newly modified cars. The boys were proud of their handiwork.

Jeremy had gone for a rather different solution.

RRMMMBLL

James's car looked identical from the outside. What had he done to modify it for the desert and the mountains?

What I've done to **prepare** for the desert is, **er,** team a rather fetching hooded **cardigan** with some old combat trousers... and put some **big wheels** on my car!

As they headed out of La Paz, Jeremy and Richard looked very pleased with their new taller, off-roadier cars. But after a few miles, their smiles wore off. Jeremy radioed Richard on the walkie-talkies.

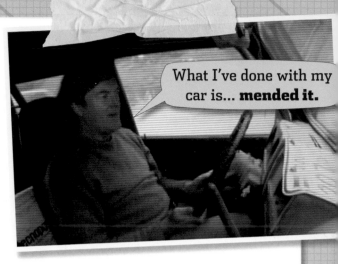

What I've done with my car is... **mended it.**

"Hammond, I've made my car worse," he admitted.

"How?" replied Richard.

"It won't ride properly, and the tyres are catching on the wheel arches, and it's got no power any more..."

Richard wasn't doing much better in his Toyota.

Now it was James's turn to look smug. His Suzuki was working perfectly, and as they climbed onto the Altiplano, he could relax and admire the amazing scenery.

I am having to **work** my engine quite hard. With **bigger wheels** on, it has the effect of gearing it up. Starting in first gear is like starting in third, and **it's hard work.** I've rather **ruined** it.

## DID YOU KNOW?

The Altiplano is found at the widest point in the Andes, and is one of the highest plateaus – a flat area within mountains – in the world. It stands almost two miles above sea level, and can reach temperatures as low as -20°C!

**Look** at that sky. That's **one of the best** skies I've seen for a very long time.

I know what you're thinking, and **I'm fine.**

On and on they drove, climbing ever higher onto the Altiplano.

"James?" Jeremy asked over the walkie-talkies. "Does it get hotter or colder when you're at altitude? I've forgotten."

"I'm pretty sure..." replied James, laughing, "that it becomes much hotter. No, sorry, colder."

"Well, there's only one way we can accurately determine what temperature it is, and that's by talking to our colleague," said Jeremy, glancing in his rear view mirror to Richard behind.

The temperature dropped further as night fell. Richard, in his roofless, doorless Toyota, decided the only solution was to wear every piece of clothing he had brought. Thankfully, this didn't make him look at all ridiculous...

It's **absolutely** breathtaking.
**Look at it.**

There's **no** breath to take
away. We're at **14,000 feet,**
according to the gizmo.

It's certainly **taken
my breath away.**

# DAY EIGHT

The next morning, the boys awoke on the Bolivian High Plains. The scenery was, thought Jeremy, staggeringly beautiful.

"Fourteen thousand feet?" wheezed Jeremy in disbelief. Richard showed him the screen of their GPS device.

"Fourteen thousand and six feet," confirmed Richard.

"What's this?" asked James, attaching a small plastic clip to the end of his finger.

"That measures your 'Sats'," said Jeremy, taking the clip from him and putting it round his own finger.

## DID YOU KNOW?
The Andes are the longest mountain range in the world. They stretch from the top of South America to the bottom, over 4,300 miles long and over 400 miles wide in places. The highest peak in the Andes is Aconcagua, which stands 22,841 feet high. That makes it the world's tallest mountain outside the Himalayas!

"I think it's something to with how much oxygen there is in your red blood cells. If it's less than 98 or 99, you've had it."

"What's yours?" asked James.

"Eighty-seven," Jeremy read from the clip. "Try yours. I bet you can't get it to go lower than 87. That's how ill I am."

James attached the clip to his index finger. "Eighty-nine," he read.

"You're nearly dead," said Jeremy. "I am dead."

Richard took his own reading. "Eighty-eight," he read, slowly. "I'm not much better."

"If you went into a doctor's surgery in England with a reading of 88," said Jeremy, grimly, "they'd put you in hospital."

"Eighty-four," read Hammond, taking another measurement.

The only thing in a worse state than the boys' red blood cells was Richard's car.

"I've broken my front right spring," he revealed, still fiddling with the plastic clip. "Completely sheared it off at both ends."

"You're joking?" said Jeremy, getting up to inspect the front right wheel of the Toyota.

So that... is meant to be **connected** to that?

**Yep.** And it's **snapped** clean off.

The boys realised they needed to lift the Toyota's front right wheel off the ground in order to fix it, but they didn't have a jack large enough to raise the now-really-quite-tall Land Cruiser. James came up with an ingenious solution. He tied the winch cable to the left-hand side of the Toyota's roll cage, and winched it in a few feet. The Land Cruiser heaved and groaned and, finally, lifted its right side off the ground. But this presented another problem.

There aren't many roadside mechanics at 14,000 feet. In fact, there are none. So it took the boys all morning to fix Richard's very broken Toyota themselves.

> Your prop shaft has **fallen off.**

By lunchtime, they had managed to repair the ailing Land Cruiser, and they set out towards the Chilean border. They made good ground, and – for once – everything was running smoothly... apart from James driving into a village well. This was a minor hitch, though, and for first time in their week-long journey, the boys were finally able to relax on the road.

> I'm in a **fantastic desert** with my two mates, all the cars are working, and it's great. **It's an adventure!**

The road was flat and smooth, and they skimmed happily towards the edge of Bolivia. With a mile to go until they reached Chile, and the roads empty as far as the eye could see, they drove three abreast, grinning with happiness and, in truth, a lack of oxygen.

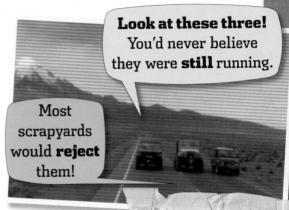

**Look at these three!** You'd never believe they were **still** running.

Most scrapyards would **reject** them!

As they crossed into Chile, the scenery became even more spectacular. The three cars sped along the road over the Altiplano, cutting between craggy, snow-topped peaks and glassy lakes. Richard, despite feeling colder than he'd ever felt before, even had time to admire the wildlife.

## DID YOU KNOW?

Chile is the seventh-largest country in South America. It is three times the size of the UK, but it's a very strange shape: though almost 4,700 miles long, it is, on average, just over 100 miles wide.

**Flamingos!** Those are actually flamingos! I've never **seen** them in the wild. **Wow!**

But the road was still climbing. With one eye on the GPS device, Jeremy gave them a countdown over the walkie-talkie.

"Forty-five feet to go... thirty feet to go," he recited. "Five, four, thr— we're there! Fifteen thousand feet! We are now higher than the highest peak in Europe, and we're still driving."

Cheering, they sped onward and upward, watching the numbers rise on the GPS as the sun sank behind the mountains and the road climbed higher and higher into the clouds...

PZZZEOooWwww!

# DAY NINE

**T**he boys knew, as they woke shivering in their tents the next morning, that the altitude would cause them problems in the day ahead.

But, just a couple of miles after they'd set off along the dusty road, they encountered a much more immediate one. The clutch on Richard's Toyota packed up, making starting, stopping and changing gear very difficult.

**Come on!** It won't come out of gear. **I'm trying to rock it... right,** we're away. Into second... match the road speed.

*Awesome Adventures: South America*

The broken clutch had cost Richard time. Jeremy and James had been stopped by the side of the road for twenty minutes when the Land Cruiser finally came lurching up the narrow track, kicking up dust as it went.

"Hammond!" cheered Jeremy as Richard coasted to a halt beside them. "The donkey lives! We're back as a three..."

But the boys had a decision to make.

"We can either go that way," wheezed Jeremy, pointing towards the track winding off into the distance, "which is very long. Or we can go that way... which is over an active volcano."

He pointed up a steep slope, behind which lay a row of giant mountains. The air was frighteningly thin already at this height. All three of the boys were panting, unable to get enough oxygen into their bodies – did they really want to go any higher? Would they even be able to breathe up there? And would the volcano erupt? Surely the long route was the sensible option?

"Short," said Richard decisively.

"Volcano," confirmed James.

"I agree," Jeremy said. Altitude or no altitude, volcano or no volcano, they were taking the direct route.

We are definitely the **highest motorists** in the world.

They set off up the steep trail, climbing higher and higher as they went. The air became thinner and thinner, and all three of the boys became dizzy with the altitude and lack of oxygen. They felt like they'd just run a marathon. Jeremy's GPS device clicked past 15,400 feet.

At this dizzying height, it was tough enough just to concentrate on keeping the car in a straight line. But Richard had more to worry about: nursing his broken car.

"Hammond's really got to think ahead with no clutch," thought James out loud. Altitude did that to you. "And he's got to think ahead with a brain starved of oxygen..."

Richard was thinking out loud too. "It'll be frightening when I need to grab first gear to get up a steep bit," he mused as he bumped over the rocky path. "Because changing down is harder. You've got to guess how high the engine will need to be revving, and slot the gear lever in... without a clutch."

But still the road climbed. The air got thinner and thinner, and every moment, however tiny, made the boys breathless. But they weren't the only ones suffering from the lack of oxygen. Their cars were too.

Up at this height, this engine is **really struggling.** For every litre of fuel vapour it gets through, it needs fourteen litres of air. **And there isn't any.** So it's just like me – **out of breath** – and that means it's so **down on power.**

In the least powerful car, James was finding the climb even tougher. His Suzuki, he guessed, was putting out, at maximum, 20bhp. You could buy scooters with more power than that!

But still they climbed. Jeremy's GPS ticked past 16,000 feet. Over three miles above sea level! They were – and there was no other word to describe it – high.

They hit a flat section of terrain, and pulled to a halt to catch their breath. Unfortunately, there wasn't any breath to catch.

**Even talking is hard work!**

**I'm feeling really quite weird...**

**My head is spinning. I've got room-spin.**

**KKRNTCH**

They had to press on. Jeremy's GPS clicked on to 16,300 feet as the road narrowed to a rough track cut into the side of the jagged, rocky volcano. As they climbed and climbed, all three of the boys were pondering the same question: which would give out first – their cars... or their bodies?

"Come on, come on!" Richard encouraged his Toyota, which was down to just a few horsepower and crunching horribly through every gearshift. "Every gear change is so critical now that I get tense about it, and that raises my heart rate. And then I need oxygen all the more..."

## DID YOU KNOW?

There are over 200 active volcanoes in the Andes. One of the biggest eruptions in recent years was from the Chilean volcano of Chaiten in May 2008. Over 5000 people had to be evacuated as ash poured from the volcano. It was Chaiten's first eruption in almost 10,000 years!

"Are you there, Hammond?" James voice crackled over the walkie-talkie.

"Yeah, I'm having to go slow," replied Richard, "because I daren't change up to third gear. I don't think I'll make it."

Jeremy, who had been listening in, joined the radio conversation. "OK, we'll slow down," he said. "We're a team up here. This isn't funny."

"Jeremy's talking about being a team?" said Richard, confused.

"Must be the altitude..."

At 16,700 feet, the engine of Richard's Toyota coughed to a halt. He couldn't restart it. Jeremy and James pulled over to help – because they were, after all, a team – and immediately regretted the decision.

They decided the Range Rover was the most likely to start. James and Richard pushed the car down a slope while Jeremy did his best to jump-start the engine. The effort left them panting and breathless, but it worked – the Range Rover

James can't get his **engine started,** I can't get **mine** started. They haven't got **any air.**

was alive! Its big engine fired reluctantly into life, and Jeremy set about shoving the Suzuki and the Toyota to get them started. The most unreliable car in the world was saving the day... again.

So, again, the boys continued to climb. 17,000 feet now, and all three of them were suffering. They all had splitting headaches, and Jeremy's lips were tingling. That couldn't be a good sign.

**Go on...** go on... **oh yeah!**

## DID YOU KNOW?

Altitude sickness is a serious illness that affects many visitors to high areas. It is mainly caused by the lack of oxygen in the air: at altitude, air pressure is lower so there is less oxygen available for the body to take in. It commonly occurs above 8,000 feet – no wonder the boys felt strange at 17,000 feet!

"I get the feeling something's going to give soon..." said Richard, nervously. All three of them knew they were in trouble. They could barely think, and their reactions were slow. If something went wrong, would they be able to think quickly enough to stop it? It seemed unlikely.

At 17,200 feet, they pulled over again and staggered from their cars, gasping for air. Jeremy looked up at the tip of the volcano looming in front of them. They still had hundreds of feet to climb.

Reluctantly, the boys all knew it was the right decision to turn back and take the long route round the volcano.

Even if the cars could get over the volcano, **I can't.** Pushing on is **stupid.** I'm calling it a day.

I think you're **right.**

Any higher, and they'd be in real danger. So they turned the cars round and charged back down the path in a desperate search for air.

"With every foot we descend," Jeremy gasped as they bumped and rattled down the track, "the engines are going to run smoother. My body's going to run smoother..."

The long route was indeed long, but it was much easier. Drunk on oxygen, the boys bolted over the rough, rocky terrain in their battered old 4x4s... and eventually reached the western edge of the Andes. They'd crossed one of the world's greatest mountain ranges.

You can **bite off** pieces and **chew** them!

It's **like** breathing soup!

Air!

It's **like** lung nectar.

"There's just one thing that's occurred to me, chaps," realised Jeremy, surveying their surroundings. "Where the hell are we?"

They were in one of the strangest places in the world, a dead, rocky plain that looked like the surface of the moon and stretched as far as the eye could see in every direction. They were in the Atacama Desert, where there is no life at all. Not even plants. Not even bacteria. Richard Hammond, thought Jeremy, was the smallest living organism for thousands of miles.

It was an infinite expanse of nothingness. No trees, no water, no animals. Nothing. Apart from an amazing road: the Pan-American Highway.

**The running is smooth and the view is spectacular!**

They were flying. Not literally, of course, but the boys were, for the first time in days, on a proper stretch of tarmac, and picking up the pace. They blasted along the Pan-American Highway, amazed by the scenery and happy to be ticking down the miles to the Pacific. It would all be plain sailing now, surely?

EEEEEYOOWWWW

Not quite. After a couple of hours of smooth, incident-free driving, Richard's car emitted an almighty clunk and lost all power. Richard drew to a halt by the side of the highway.

**Oh dear.** What's happened there is that your **prop shaft** has **fallen off.**

It didn't **sound** good.

This was bad news. Richard walked back down the highway and retrieved his broken bits of car – at which point he realised that his mechanical problems were even worse than he had first thought. Not only was his propshaft broken, but his differential was completely shattered too.

"Good God!" exclaimed James, peering under the Toyota at the mass of split bent metal. "I'm surprised that didn't somersault the car!"

Thankfully Jeremy didn't stop to help, which meant that – with the aid of lots of spanners and several buckets of grease – Richard and James were able to repair the Toyota in just an hour. Sort of...

James and Richard caught up with Jeremy, and the convoy charged on through the desert. They were now tantalisingly close to the Pacific, their finish line.

It's now running **front-wheel** drive only. So it's just the front legs, **dragging** the Toyota along. But it's **still** working!

"There can be no doubt that this has been our toughest assignment ever," Jeremy thought out loud. "No question about that. It's nearly killed us, and it's nearly killed our cars."

But it hadn't. Their cheap, rubbish 4x4s, bought unseen on the Internet, had crossed the Amazon rainforest, scaled the most dangerous road in the world, and they'd still been working when their drivers had broken down in the Andes. With the finish line nearly in sight, the boys realised that they didn't just respect their cars: they loved them.

"I have a teddy bear," continued Jeremy, thoughtfully. "I've had it since the day I was born. One of its arms has fallen off, one of its eyes is missing, and its head has come off more times than I can mention. To you, it would be worthless junk, but to me, it means everything. And it's the same story with this car..."

James was just as full of praise for his Suzuki.

The ride is **terrible,** it's a bit noisy, it doesn't handle that well and **I'm always worried** that it's going to fall over. But it has done everything the **big boys** have done, it hasn't got stuck any more often, and the **only** time it has really gone **wrong** was a result of its **dunking** in the river. The **plucky** little car has done **alright.**

Richard was just as emotional about his grubby Toyota. They were just 40 miles from the Pacific now. They could almost taste the salt air... but something was wrong. The road was rising, not dropping. They were 2,300 feet above sea level, and still climbing. Surely they would start going downhill soon?

From the very **start** of the trip, when I couldn't start it on the raft, I thought **'oh no'.** But I didn't know it then. I didn't know how **determined** it was. It's a **great little car.**

I can **smell...** a boiling engine.

No. The punishing climb went on and on, and the cars were suffering.

"Is it a sheer drop at the other end?" asked Jeremy over the walkie-talkie. "We're nearly at the Pacific now, and we're 4,000 feet up!"

As he spoke, they turned off the highway and headed over the dunes towards the finish line. They were now just a couple of miles from the sea, but unfortunately there was one more obstacle in the way. A big one.

"Hang on a minute!" shouted Jeremy. He hauled on his handbrake, and James and Richard ground to a stop next to him. Straight ahead of them was an impossibly steep sand dune, descending 4,000 feet – nearly a mile! – straight into the sea.

**DID YOU KNOW?**
The Pacific is the world's biggest ocean. It stretches all the way from Asia and Australia in the west to North and South American in the east... and makes up thirty per cent of the world's surface area!

"What happens if you dig in?" asked James, peering nervously over the edge.

"If you dug in and started to roll," said Jeremy grimly. "The chances of you being alive at the bottom are... nil."

It was terrifying. But the boys knew they had no choice but to descend the dune, so they decided to practise first on a smaller dune. They drove to the top of a sandy bank, and lined up their cars.

Jeremy counted down on walkie-talkie. "Three, two, one—"

"Hang on!" shouted Richard. He jumped from his Toyota and jogged over to Jeremy's Range Rover. "Before we do this, I wanted to say—"

But he was cut off mid-sentence by a shout from James. As Richard was stood by Jeremy's car, the handbrake on his Toyota had failed, and it was now gathering pace as it rolled down the giant dune. And then it started to flip.

Richard set off, sprinting down the dune behind his beloved Toyota, but it was too late. The Land Cruiser rolled and crashed and flipped its way down the dune, smashing into pieces as it went.

"My donkey!" yelled Richard forlornly, as he reached the Toyota, which had dug into the sand and come to rest far down the dune. "Its wheel's come off!"

The donkey was dead. Well and truly dead. Richard stood silently, crestfallen, by the side of his wrecked Toyota. It was all over. But on the bright side, at least he wouldn't have to drive down the Giant Dune of Death!

James and Jeremy didn't have a choice. They lined up their cars at the top of the dune. They weren't nervous. They were petrified.

> This is **utterly, utterly stupid.**

**27**

Richard had scrambled back to the top of the dune to watch their descent.

"Are you ready, James?" he asked over walkie-talkie.

"Are we going for second gear, Jezza?" radioed James.

"Second gear, low range... have you got your diff lock set?" replied Jeremy, checking everything was correctly set on his Range Rover.

"I haven't got a diff lock!" James said. Too late to do anything about that.

"Best of luck, boys," Hammond decided it was time for them to tackle the dune. "Three, two, one... go!"

And over the edge they went.

## DID YOU KNOW?

A diff lock – or locking differential – helps a car to grip better by stopping its wheels from spinning out of control. But only if you have one on your car!

Jeremy and James plunged down the dune, fighting to keep control as their wheels dug into the sand and their cars slewed sideways. It was scary, scarier even than the Death Road. And they were getting faster.

And faster. And faster. With no way of slowing down, James and Jeremy shot down the dune, out of control and slipping around. If one of their wheels dug too far into the sand now, they would flip and, in all probability, die. They gripped their steering wheels desperately, bouncing and sliding down the sheer dune.

"It's going a bit fast now!" yelled Jeremy, clinging on for dear life.

"A 900-year-old, utterly ruined Range Rover... it's levelling out! It's levelling out!"

And it was. As the dune flattened off, Jeremy and James wrestled their cars under control and eased off, whooping as they coasted down to the edge of the Pacific. They'd made it! They'd done it! Well, two of them had...

The three boys were reunited at the water's edge, the sun sinking deep in the sky and glinting off the ocean. Richard, despite the fact that his Land Cruiser was smashed into hundreds of pieces higher up the dune, and despite the fact he'd had to cover the last few miles on foot, was still adamant he'd made a good choice of car.

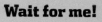

Wait for me!

**Rubbish.** It has been a constant source of **problems** and **delays.**

My car was **extraordinarily good.** It led a very **hard life** and it died a **noble death.** It was **valiant.**

**Yes,** but it was **old** and **arthritic** and it'd been **beaten** every day of its life...

These **two cars** are old and arthritic, and **they made it.**

"Can I just make the case for the Suzuki?" James continued the 'which car won' discussion. "It was a plucky little car – it helped you out a few times. It technically never really broke down."

"It didn't survive very well in the puddle," corrected Jeremy.

"But most importantly... the ride is rotten," concluded James.

"Yes, because it has ruined your spine, and because yours isn't here," Jeremy pointed a finger at Hammond, "we have a startling conclusion. It turns out that most unreliable car in the world... is the most reliable car in the world!"

James and Richard started laughing.

"No one expected that, did they?" grinned Richard.

> Ladies and gentlemen, I give you... **the Range Rover!**

The sun dipped behind the horizon, casting a warm glow over the three boys and their two remaining cars. They'd made it. They'd finished.

# AWESOME ADVENTURES:

**Also Available:**

ISBN: 978-1-40590-699-9